THE
PRACTICAL
ALCHEMIST

Copyright © 1988 by Christopher Manson
All rights reserved, including the right to reproduce
this book or portions thereof in any form.
Published by Henry Holt and Company, Inc.,
115 West 18th Street, New York, New York 10011.
Published in Canada by Fitzhenry & Whiteside Limited,
195 Allstate Parkway, Markham, Ontario L3R 4T8.

Library of Congress Cataloging-in-Publication Data
Manson, Christopher.
The practical alchemist : showing the way an ordinary house cat
may be transformed into true gold / Christopher Manson.
    p.   cm.
"An Owl book."
ISBN 0-8050-0455-6 (pbk.)
1. Anagrams.   I. Title.
GV1507.A5M36   1988
793.73 — dc19   87-17751
                      CIP

First Edition

Designed by Susan Hood
Printed in the United States of America
1 3 5 7 9 10 8 6 4 2

ISBN 0-8050-0455-6

THE
PRACTICAL
ALCHEMIST

*Showing the way an ordinary house cat
may be transformed into true gold*

CHRISTOPHER MANSON

An Owl Book

UNA ARBOR · MULTI RAMI

HENRY HOLT AND COMPANY
NEW YORK

An Introduction to *The Practical Alchemist*

Their chiefest study was to wrap up their Secrets in Fables, and spin out their Fancies in Vailes and Shadows, whose Radii seemed to extend every way, yet so, that they meet at a Common Center, and point only at one Thing.

So said Elias Ashmole, a seventeenth-century writer about the books of the great Alchemists . . . and this book is no different.

Like all good alchemy, *The Practical Alchemist* is about the transformation of one thing into another; in this case you can transform the word CAT into the word GOLD. Instead of blazing furnaces and toxic chemicals you need only a pencil and paper to carry out this Great Work.

Beginning with the word CAT, which you see illustrated on the following spread, you will find that it can be transformed into several different words, illustrated in step one. The words illustrated in step one, in their turn, are transformed into other words illustrated in step two, and so on throughout the book.

The words are transformed by means of the simple Operations listed below:

ANAGRAM: The letters in the word are rearranged (CAT to ACT, for instance).

ADD ONE: A letter is added to the word (ACT to FACT).

CHANGE ONE: A letter in the word is changed for another (FACT to FACE).

DROP ONE: A letter is subtracted from the word (FACE to ACE).

The challenge to you, as a literary Alchemist, is to successfully forge a chain of forty-five transformations from the beginning of the book to the end. There are any number of word chains illustrated in the book that lead from CAT in step one to GOLD on the last page, but there is only *one* chain that lets you turn your CAT to GOLD without repeating a word.

You may use only one of the four Operations for each transformation, and the new word you make must always be one that you can find illustrated on that page. (Adding an S to make the plural or taking an S away to make the singular both count as making a new word, and are allowed.) All the words used are nouns or can be phrased as nouns.

At the end you should have a list of forty-five different words beginning with CAT and ending in GOLD.

For example, in step one you can find the words BAT, HAT, CAP, CART, ACT, CAST, and COT illustrated as your first choice to make. Say you choose the word CAP: in step two you can find a COP. . . . Perhaps you can find the next link in step three, and so on to the end of the book. Or perhaps not. There are hundreds of words illustrated in the book and many dividing and connecting chains. . . . Some go all the way to the end, some go nowhere. This is, in fact, a labyrinth of words.

The "Discourse of Mercury," which accompanies the illustrations, contains clues to the correct words. To help you decipher the clues I herewith provide you with your very own "Philosopher's Stone," the mystical adjunct necessary for the true Golden Transformation, as all good Alchemists know.

An Alchemist sat in his workshop after working for many days and nights, to meditate on his failure to transmute anything into Gold. Being weary from his labors he fell into a deep sleep and, behold! . . . the Spirit of Mercury appeared to him and said: "I have come to thee to show thee the Way, that thou mayest achieve that Work, which so many have not." In his sleep the Alchemist was amazed and said: "Good Spirit, what will you show me?" Mercury swept aside the veils of dream to reveal a panorama of strange landscapes, characters, and objects in a bewildering and visionary world. "If thou art of noble Mind and quick Wit I will show to thee the Receipes and Operations whereby any base or common thing may be ennobled and transformed into pure and sparkling Gold! Anything may be so worked upon . . . even this, thy Cat! Remember: as it is in the Microcosm, so it is in the Macrocosm. Arise! I shall be thy Guide through all this Realm of Emblem and Allegory, that thou mayest learn and profit from the Secrets of the Great Work!" And, so saying, the Spirit of Mercury took up the sleeping Alchemist and his CAT and bore them away through the mists of dream.

Here begins the Discourse of Mercury.

A small theater is our first vision, meaning we must set the Stage for all the Works to follow. Dost thou see thy Cat? He is here . . . and here . . . and here, too. He is truly all around us; he has been transformed into several Shapes and Guises and is hid under many false faces. Here we must choose what props we may take up or lay down, for the work we will perform will o'er-top all that thee hast assayed before. Take up only that which thou mayest carry away with thee: that is, a sense of Balance, the ability to grasp several Facts at one time, and the Will to strike out all erroneous Ideas. For such props as these, thou shalt require no servants, or porters or wheeled conveyance.

STEP 1

A weapon thrown into this Room is a Symbol of the need to add sharp, vinegary substances to the Body of that which thou would transform. In this be ruled by the Laws which thou hast studied. . . . Leave nothing to Chance. Here is thy Cat exhibited in his second transformation, and the Course that thou must plot is plainly shown. Know that all things, all Bodies, are like the Earth itself, wherein a planted seed may germinate and sprout. The seed of Gold may be planted in any Substance, nurtured and purified, so that it grows and flourishes to our Purpose. So, place the Matter that thou makest into an ordinary Container, and bathe it in Vinegar, recalling always that the Work must begin at the closing instant of the Day, and that all these Operations be made and accomplished by the Hand.

STEP 2

The absence of both moon and stars dismays thee, I see it plain. This Noah is a reflection of that which brings the Complimentary Pairs, or Principles, together and protects them, and allows the product of these Unions to emerge from our Vessel. 🐈 Carry over what thou hast made before, and thou wilt find the Pickling Bath has caused the Body to change its Outer Semblance. Preserve the Body in its original Vessel, allowing the Outside to separate from the Inside. Though difficult to see, the Separation may be discovered if thou wilt divide the Top from the Bottom. 🐈 Thou wilt find thy way to greater Prominence if thou dost not wait for ordinary light. . . . See all before thee by means of that which thou seekest. There are, truly, many sorts of illumination.

STEP 3

A short time after this the Matter must be partly uncovered, and allowed to lie fallow in preparation for our Cultivation. The quiet Walks thou seest before thee are Symbol of the need for Study and Contemplation . . . all which must hang from the double hook of Inquiry and Experimentation. Only thus wilt thou be enabled to avoid Snares and leap over Obstacles. Grind the Substance in the Wheels of a mill, taking care that no Scraps or Residues remain. Mix these with Brine and stir all with a pointed weapon.

STEP 4

What we see now are the Vessels required for the following stages of the Work. Harmony must be maintained between the Nature of the Mixture and the type of container most apt for its Operation. Only then will the Portal open to further Progress. By your soaking the Mixture in its watery bath, the Animal Spirits in it will begin to stir and to rise up to the top, and so be drawn off. Then shall the raiment of the Matter be renewed and its Baser Elements left behind. Before thee are three of the Principle Elements: Earth, Water, and Air. It remains for us to supply the Fourth. For now . . . walk on!

STEP 5

Restrict thyself from meddling overmuch with the Natural Reactions in the Vessel. As this Creature is Confined for future use, let nothing now escape from the Mixture — only divide it into Three Parts, and let One Part stand idle, One Part be supported by the addition of fermented Spirits, and the Last Part drained off into a suitable container and tightly stoppered up. To allow the First and Second Parts to ascend to a Higher Plane on the Great Chain, they must be continually stirred up and no other matter allowed to mix with them. To accomplish this thou must needs be willing to relinquish the Support normally derived from sleeping and, if necessary, from eating.

STEP 6

Half a moment after sunrise thou wilt open up the prison containing the Third Part of the Mixture and, as is illustrated here, bring the Three Parts of it together, all at the same instant. In the tumult of their coming at one another the harmful Vapors arising therefrom will be carried off, and the several parts ploughed back into the Whole, each one into the other. In Emblematic terms, the Hermit's Wisdom, unpolluted through the grace of his seclusion on the Mountain, must be joined to the Animal Elements, so that the Summit of success be attained. They cannot be forever cut in twain . . . but a true Union can be effected only by the utmost Balance of this matching Pair.

STEP *7*

An article which must be procured is pictured here, in the midst of this great storm of Wind. The Matter must be buried in the Earths which are obtainable only in certain Latitudes (that thou knowest well) and then Baked so completely that all remaining unstable Spirits be removed. The Fire thou usest must be blown up to ensure the Heat will support the task. If, by Chance, thou must knock on the Door of Wisdom several times to gain admittance, let not the Tally of thy attempts discourage thee! Thou must first of all be divested of thine Errors and Fallacies, even as the Spirits of the Dead are divested, when they leave this World, of clothing.

STEP 8

Baked as I have directed, the Body will be reduced in Quantity and dried, so that thou wilt be able to stir it up and rake it back and forth, until the Heel of Time has ground it quite to Powder. Thou shalt take up newly-made Vessels, never used before for any other purpose, and cause equal amounts of the Powder to be laid in the bottom of two such Vessels, in such proportions as thou knowest. Recall that, though this demands of thee infinite travail from the Outset to the Finish, thou wilt be so Rewarded as to be forever secure in all thy Properties and Goods!

STEP 9

ood is needful for thine own nourishment, and so it is required as well for the Body thou makest at this stage of the Work. To encourage an increase in fertility first pour on Brine again, little by little, as the Powder is able to drink it up, but never more at one time than can be quickly and readily taken up by it. The Powder, being very dry and sandy, will seek to consume the moisture incontinently, and thou must observe that the moisture is evenly applied and no one part is surfeited before another. If thou canst leap over this Obstacle (which many fail to do) then will the Matter be fortified for the next step. Convey the Bodies in thy Vessels away from the Fire, and set thy workshop up so that thou mayest strike away any Barriers to the flow from the one Vessel to the other. Now is the time for an infusion of spirits, both Celestial and Animal.

STEP 10

A short time after this add the Venom of several sorts of Animals, taken from the Three Zones of Earth, in just Proportions to the one Vessel, and the aged Lees of Wine to the other. The Vision shows thee an Emblem of the Two Aspects inherent in the Mixture — its appearance on the Surface, and the naked Truth that is hid beneath. This duality is present in thee and in all things under the influence of the Sun. No matter how thou seekest to fortify or to protect thyself, or to stimulate thy senses . . . no matter which way the Wind shall blow, everything thou hast done has its Reflection in the Great World, the Macrocosm. Take note! When thou hast added in these needful Substances, then shalt thou carefully stir them all together, using only thine own Hand, or some other Living Thing, such as a wooden stick.

STEP 11

Furniture of War, of Travel, and Emblems of the Farm and the Hunt are now shown to thee. As all men seek a return to that Garden, wherefrom they were Expelled, in the midst of thy Worldly Pursuits thou must strive to bring thy Work full Circle to a state near that of its inception. Therefore, bury it again, and wash it again, and when thou hast done this the Body will be reborn and grow apace. Thou mayest advance no further if thou hast dulled thy senses with immoderate Drink, or hast otherwise proved thyself unworthy to know these Secrets. Trust in the Rightness of thy Purpose, cross any Barrier, eschew all tawdry diversions, and let this Work be thy sole support.

STEP 12

Part of thy Mixture must be allowed to fall into a Protective enclosure and lie Dormant, while the other part be infused with one of the Noble Elements, fixed to a Pole of thirty cubits and carried on until, a storm occurring, it be purified and amalgamated by the Stroke of Zeus. To attain the Summit of Perfection in all things thou must show an Obstinacy and Determination seldom found in Man. Surrounded by the Treasury of Wisdom, still he seeks like one blind, for a fragment of knowledge here and there. He cannot see the Forest for a Tree.

STEP 13

Faithful to my Pledge I have shown thee all things necessary to begin the next Phase. In a large wooden Vessel place the Three Noble Elements, according to the Laws thou hast studied. Add fresh Water, not Brine, which has been conducted to this place through mountain rocks, and boil it all up until the Scales which have formed on the surface of the Body shall be rolled away, and polluting Vapors fly off. If thou wilt follow all these, my Precepts, be assured that I will ever be thy Friend.

STEP 14

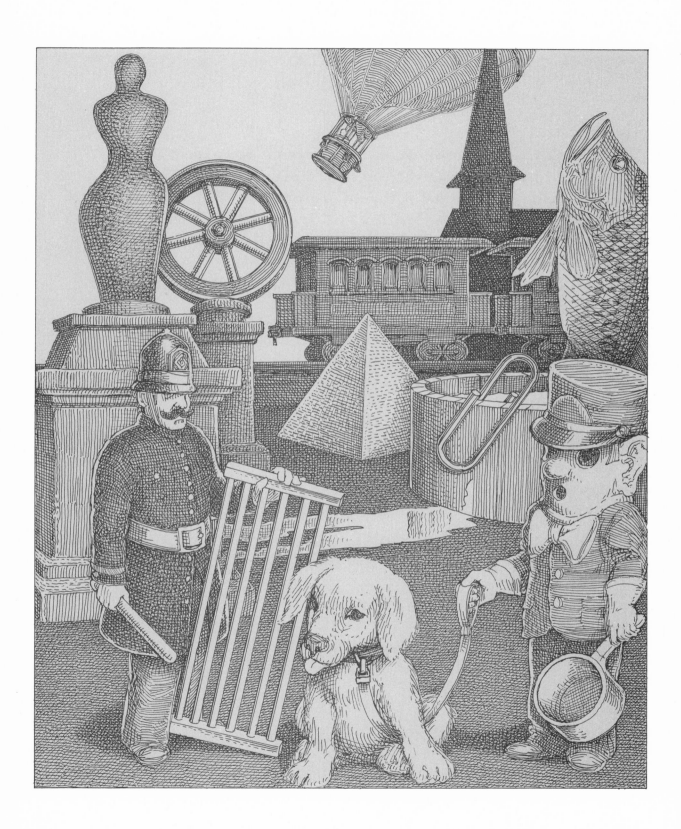

Archæological excavations revealing statues of great antiquity are illustrated here to show thee how deeply thou must delve beneath the Surface of thy Studies. Thus, a Greater World that is hid behind a fence of Iron shall be revealed to thee. Crush the Matter next with a stout hammer, or mallet, and mix it all up with the fermented milk of cattle. Allow any impurities to be carried off by evaporation, and the Body's natural Heat-producing activity.

STEP 15

Great and Marvellous are the Visions I have shown thee! But see that the riches thou hopest to accumulate can be nibbled away by low, corrupting influences if the Body is not shut up in a protective Chest or some impermeable Jar. Here it can be preserved from the adverse influences of unsuitable Planetary Configurations. Think hard and thou wilt come upon the point I have been driving at. After any evil Planets have waned, decant the Mixture into another Vessel that has some small vents set in diverse places at the top, that Vapors thrown off by the heat of the Reaction not exert such undue pressures, that the Vessel may explode with much fire and sound!

STEP 16

A place to repose under a shady tree is now pictured. Observe the base Creatures that disport themselves, using the Furnishings and Utensils of Man. . . . They know not what they may accomplish, yet will they play at the Great Work, understanding nothing. So like to them are all other Alchemists, save for thee, who hast merited my protection and Assistance. When the Reactions are subsided, empty the Vessel to the last trace of moisture, and tying up the Matter in a net, or sack, allow it to de-compose under the rays of the Sun. This natural Baking should take three days and cannot be interrupted. The sack will serve thee well to keep unwanted things out and, at the same time, keep things in.

STEP 17

The source of the next transformation is plainly shown. The Substance must be suddenly turned over, taken out of its sack and cleansed. Allow it to completely dry. In color the outside will appear dark and green but, when cut apart, will reveal a dry yellow color within. If thou has worked under the influence of the most benign Zodiacal Signs, thou needst have no fear of failure. Procure that Sovereign Medicine that thou hast learned of before. . . . Now is the time to add this powerful link to our growing chain. Pay heed to all Signs and Portents. . . . On this score we have no more need of words.

STEP 18

Clothing the Body in its Proper Vestment is our next subject. If thou wilt only cut up the Body, as is shown, a fumigation will drive off unwanted elements and further purify it. Allow the Body to lie dormant in a Vessel that is whole and sound for the space of time it takes the Sun to sail around the World. During all this time the mixture should be carefully watched. . . . Never take thine eyes away from it . . . and gently stir it up if it shows signs of drying out. Thou must not leave off thy Ministrations at this point, for the Body is here vulnerable to many ills. Your Role should be that of a Guardian or a Protector.

STEP 19

Penetrating the Secrecy that Shrouds these Emblems requires a sharp Wit and a keen understanding. 🐈 Now see that the Matter is strained through some Fabric into a Glass Container and evenly diluted with Brine and Sharp Oil, so that it is increased three-fold. If the plant is to grow and stand on its own, my secret Meaning must be comprehended . . . otherwise the strength and Vitality of the Plant will flag. During this Operation any acrid Vapors which might otherwise consume the Body in its entirety will fly off, and herein lies the point.

STEP 20

Made by an oven's Fires, yet still inwardly susceptible to the Power of Generative Warmth, the Body is now sufficiently purified. Thou shouldst keep straightly all thy accounts of exactly what quantities have been added and what has been lost. The robust Animal Heats in the Body should be alternately soothed and stirred up. Released from their Confinement, the seeds within the Body shall now begin that ascent and growth that bring on the true transformation. This will occur only if the Signs appear in their proper Houses. When all is prepared a Vessel should be got ready to Hand that is very wide in the Mouth.

STEP 21

Flying from one House to the next, the Planets governing the Work wait for no man! Thou must work as quickly as thou canst to Chart the most Propitious Course through the Sea of Time. 🐱 Take up the Matter, and after immersion in strong Spirits, seal it up with an infusion of Horn, Bone, and shell, under the Sign shown to you here. This must all be got ready beforehand lest thy headlong progress become snagged. 🐱 The Wise Man knows that all will be spoiled and these Messages be lost if thy Work is not in Harmony with the never-ending Cycles of the Heavenly Machine.

STEP 22

Found on the surface of the Body is a scaly substance which must be re-mixed into its Parent. Plough it back into that Earth from which it came. . . . The Artful Practitioner must distinguish the true from the false. After this place the Mixture in the wide-mouthed Vessel, along with the milk of Cattle which will separate the Lighter Elements from the Heavier. . . . Those less valuable Parts will rise up to the very Top. Just as the Fat should be kept from the Lean, the Ocean be kept back from the Low-lying Land and One Sort of Beast be kept apart from the Other Sort, on a Farm.

STEP 23

Growing in Knowledge thou wilt surely see that the Path to Wisdom is steep and difficult. . . . Only those willing to make such an effort will rise above the Common Herd. At the most propitious Juncture of the Signs ruled by Mars, plunge the Body into a pool and drown it. From thy Containers of the Noble Elements add to the Pool those Substances, in those Quantities, that thou already knowest of. Take out the Body and, putting it in an Enclosure suitable to the purpose, shake it back and forth, up and down, to loosen the Matter and smooth away any roughness. . . . This is more important than any other thing!

STEP 24

Clothes hang loosely on the Wise Man who cares not for the pleasures of the Table so much as he cares for the Nourishment of his Spirit. Protected from the depradations of Fortune, from wandering in Error, he will not suffer the Imprisonment of Sloth or Ignorance as he pursues the Way. ❧ Uncover now the Matter and allow it to cool sufficiently, so that becoming durable it will not be damaged by any tool. Enclose the Matter in a bath of Honey, gathered under the influence and the Light of the Proper Stars, and thou wilt have made great progress — count upon it!

STEP 25

One Thing thou must keep in thy Mind, as thou art carried from one stage of the Journey to the next: Audacity and Fortitude shall be made One with Learning, as is shown here, and so all is Clothed in its Proper Guise. Take up the perdurable Body and to its bath of Honey add an influx of powerful Spirits and place all in the Flames of a Furnace. Thou must not omit any Thing, though it cost thee labor through both Day and Night. Cleanse and Purify thyself at this time, and know that each step being most necessary and dependent on What has gone before must be completed before thou canst move on to another.

STEP 26

Momentarily close up the Vessel wherein the Matter is heated, that all elusive Vapors required to Enrich the Body shall be snared in the Furnace. Thus will it be brought to a state of Flux where one Element contained within the Body will pursue the Other. So the stage is Set to fill thy empty Coffers! 🐈 If thou hast recorded faithfully the Quantities of Matter thou hast added and subtracted, the subsequent Tasks will seem to be Child's Play. If not, the Temple of Knowledge, built up with all thy labor, will dissolve before thine eyes!

STEP *27*

Not able to contain the Force of this Puissant Reaction, thy Furnace may crack if thou dost not cool the Mixture with Fresh Water. As there are no Vents, or should be none, it will Fire off Sparks and Smokes, but the Fire must be kept going until the Honey is altogether vanished and subsumed into the Body to soften it, and render it fit for Grinding. Reduce it to fine grains, no larger than a rodent's eye, and shake it up together with coarse Black Powder and thou wilt find that the diverse Substances do fasten, the one upon the other, and form a new Substance. As soon as this occurs be prepared for the following step. . . . Careful attention is here necessary, as the joining together will happen with dispatch, and in a moment's time there will be nothing to see.

STEP 28

Light and Darkness are two aspects of the selfsame thing, but here the lighter Part of the Body must give way to the Darker, as it is plunged once again into a pickling bath. Do not omit all the proper Ceremonies that will encourage Amenable Influences, and discourage the other Sort. Thou must have the support of the Spirits of all the Noble Elements. Take the measure of the Dark Matter which sinks and place it on a bed of dried grasses to remove any trace of moisture. Place it again on a source of Flame, which should be blown up to a high degree of heat, until the Matter assumes a Dark color.

STEP 29

One half of the Body (that half which was heated) should now be taken off the Flame and, as the Vision before us shows, the artful Practitioner should take all care that this is accomplished before the Stars reach the Meridian! Thus and so thy books have told thee. Now suddenly quench the Fire and pour the Other, Lighter half of the Body into a Vessel that will hold twice as much as thou hast placed in it. Leave this partially uncovered. Soon, thou wilt write Books enough, thyself, and all other Men shall know and acknowledge that, for thee, the Wind of Ill-Fortune is restrained!

STEP 30

Several sorts of Matter will be evident in the First Vessel. Beware now of too precipitous a Course of Action lest ye fall into Error, now that the Work has been carried to such a Length. Thy labors shall be rewarded all the more if thou hast husbanded the Quantities of Matter most carefully. Allow none of the subtle essences to be driven off, and always brush any scraps back into the heart of the Mixture, lest they be made away with by scavengers. Maintain that Harmony of the Circle, or Ring, as all the planetary Spheres do, and thou wilt be able to turn the process around as often as it pleases thee. Take care, also, of the fumes arising from the Vessels, which can wreak harm both on Animals and on People.

Hold on to that Vessel containing the Darker Body and stir it up most carefully, taking especial note to refrain from Beating or Striking the Body, as it is now unstable. Here the Vision shows thee the Narrow Way that thou must travel upon to bring all the Elements into Harmony at last. Take no chances, and see clearly that now is the time to add again the Sovereign Medicine to the Lighter Body, which will cause Smokes to rise up and fly off. Now blend the Lighter and the Darker Bodies into One, that they may sit easily together. Never deviate from this Path or these instructions, and thou art sure to succeed with this.

STEP 32

Under my tutelage thou hast so far been amply rewarded. Hold together all I have shown thee, for now comes a most critical Juncture in the planting and the Growing of this, our Golden Plant. Take the blended Matter up in a basin and see it is cooled, so that it turns all Grey, as it were a sign of Age upon a Man. Fear not . . . this is not a True, or Final, Death, but a wholly new Substance will bloom from out of the Corruption of the Old. After cooling it must be Baked again and again until a crust forms over it and thou hast seen it has been heated through from the head to the foot.

STEP 33

Young as thou art in the Great Work, thou hast progressed further down this road than many before thee. To interpret this Vision, rake off all the Scales, the Crust, and other Scraps from the Baking until the Fundamental Matter is again exposed, in the Vessel it was heated in. Dig over all these Fatty Earths, bathe the Matter again in Brine and pour off the Fluid in a separate Vessel. The Body should now exhibit Signs of Decay like unto the Body of a Man.

STEP 34

Containers of several sorts should be gathered together, even as thou seest before thee. Here the Inexperienced Practitioner will be Strongly and Evilly tempted to abridge the following steps . . . but, even if thou must steal that which is required, have no hesitation. It is not given to many to succeed, and Death is thy Common Lot. Place a fragment of Gold, now, in the Heart of the Body, that, like a very seed, it will grow and reproduce itself. Decant the Mixture into an open Vessel that will not decay with the Reaction. After a sufficient amount of time has flown by, the generative animal heats will Rise Up. . . . Then thou must procure a cover.

STEP 35

Not one whit shalt thou depart from this, the Course I have laid down for thee. This point is crucial, and it were well for thee to remember that all subsequent Firings of the Body are dependent on the reactions of the Volatile Fumes and Smokes that have been infused into the Matter ere now. Here will the quantity of the Body be Drawn Out, with the addition of Fresh Water from an appropriate Vessel. Then fire the Mixture, dry it, and grind it to the consistency of Meal. Then wilt thou see how the Seed thou hast planted has grown.

STEP 36

A collection of learned treatises forms the Foundation of a Child's Play. Thus shall thy Studies and Preparations make a Base that can support thy Growth as a most accomplished Alchemist. Plunge the Powder, or Meal, into a large Bath of Quicksilver, always stirring and cleaning it until it has solidified once more and grown cool to the touch. This will make up the Skeleton of that Golden Body which we shall raise up from the Heat of the Crucible, and so reveal that spark of the Sun's Fire that dwells within Man and is part of Animals, of Plants, and of Things.

STEP *37*

Do not fail to Fire the Matter once again, and yet again, and seal it up into a Stoppered Vessel, that the Seeds may grow as they should and so clothe the Skeleton of the Body with a most Golden raiment. Because thou hast shown such dogged Determination, nevermore shalt thou be the butt of Common jests, or any other Plays or Mockeries. Decant the Mixture into an open Pot and, using only a piece of living Wood, stir it around, until it begins to roll up upon itself in a sort of spherical bundle. Do not, through any mischance, allow any foreign Matter to fall in.

STEP 38

Cooking up the Mixture so many times in thy Workshop has insured that there is small Chance of any impurities remaining in the Golden Body. While still young, the Body is now growing rapidly and will soon exhibit a durability impervious to any tool. . . . It will not be cut, or pierced in any way. Before this happens add a further piece of Noble Metal, such as a coin, and re-fire the Whole until it (the Coin) has been all absorbed. From now on the Process will gain both Speed and Momentum, as if it were a stone running down a hill. The final Stages of the Transmutation must occur in a Wooden Vessel.

STEP 39

Green and Yellow are the principal colors of the Mixture at this time if thou hast done all correctly. All the different Elements are now tied together and speak with one Great Voice. By protecting the Mixture from Contamination and keeping it apart from all other influences, thou hast succeeded in sealing up the Beneficent Aspects of the Sun within it. From top to bottom it has been clothed in the appropriate Vestments, and no matter if a piece or two is taken off, they will continue to grow into That which thou seekest. Thou hast truly made the Body into a most wonderful Vehicle for the Germination of Gold, just as the seed is carried within the nut, or a letter is contained within its envelope.

STEP 40

Construction of the final Apparatus needed for the Work should consume all thy attention, lest thee fall into Error, like some Ignorant and Loutish fellow, shown here. Thou art near the end of thy Journey and have but three steps more to take! Now there is no time for playing with trifles or making thyself at ease, yet thou shouldst maintain a reverent and seemly Frame of Mind. See that all about thee is clean and free of Rubbish, dirt, or garbage of any sort, that thy Path be clear. Take up a sieve, or net, close-woven of strings or fibers never used before for any other thing, and wrap up the Body in it as if it were in a Bag, pouring any amount of Quicksilver over it, so the Body is well washed. Set this aside for one Phase of the Moon and retain the sieve for thy future aid.

STEP 41

Caught in the Filter of thy Apparatus the last impurities in the Body are removed. The Laws governing the Whirling of the Spheres, the Times of their Conjunctions and Influences also govern the Substances and Actions in this, our Little World. The Sun's heat nourishes the Planets; just so the Heat thou shalt now apply will bring on the final stage of the transformation. Place the Body in a flat metal container of shallow draught and place with it a modicum of each of the Noble Elements, as each House in turn becomes Home to the Star that watches over our Work. All this is shown by the calculations of thine own Diagram. Then, after this Year is passed take up thy Work and place the Matter again in thy Net.

STEP 42

Low Elements and base Materials are all born of the Sun, all are nourished by the Sun and all contain a spark of the Sun's Fire. So, when thou hast strained and purified the Body for the last time, place it in a container of metal, cover it with New Earth, and, after one more Phase of the Lunar Cycle has passed, thou mayest uncover it and . . . See! Thou wilt have attained that which all men wish for. As it is in the Macrocosm, so it is in the Microcosm. Be always Guided by this and thou shalt never go astray.

So ends the Discourse of Mercury.

STEP 43

The Alchemist awoke with a start; the Sun was just rising in the sky. Rubbing his eyes the Alchemist thought long and deeply on the marvellous Visions he had seen, and the Secrets told to him by the Spirit of Mercury. Then he remembered that his Cat had been taken up in the Dream and looking around was amazed to find the animal was no longer there! In his place a great piece of pure Gold glittered and shone in the light of the morning Sun.

The Alchemist's Formula

Each number in this solution represents a letter of the alphabet.

STEP 1	3·1·20	STEP 16	4·9·7	STEP 31	2·15·14·4
STEP 2	3·1·18·20	STEP 17	4·9·14	STEP 32	2·1·14·4
STEP 3	4·1·18·20	STEP 18	2·9·14	STEP 33	8·1·14·4
STEP 4	4·1·18·11	STEP 19	14·9·2	STEP 34	12·1·14·4
STEP 5	4·9·18·11	STEP 20	2·9·2	STEP 35	12·1·4
STEP 6	4·9·18·20	STEP 21	2·9·20	STEP 36	12·9·4
STEP 7	4·9·5·20	STEP 22	2·9·20·5	STEP 37	11·9·4
STEP 8	4·9·5	STEP 23	11·9·20·5	STEP 38	11·9·20
STEP 9	20·9·5	STEP 24	11·9·14·5	STEP 39	16·9·20
STEP 10	16·9·5	STEP 25	16·9·14·5	STEP 40	16·15·20
STEP 11	16·9·7	STEP 26	12·9·14·5	STEP 41	16·15·4
STEP 12	16·5·7	STEP 27	12·9·14·11	STEP 42	8·15·4
STEP 13	12·5·7	STEP 28	2·12·9·14·11	STEP 43	3·15·4
STEP 14	12·15·7	STEP 29	2·12·9·14·4	STEP 44	3·15·12·4
STEP 15	4·15·7	STEP 30	2·12·15·14·4	STEP 45	7·15·12·4